# In the Doghouse

## Angela Roscoe

supported by north west arts board


Illustrations, Mike Carter
Cover design, David Andrassy
Back cover photograph, Patricia Duffin
Editor, Patricia Duffin
Published and distributed by Gatehouse Books Ltd
Hulme Adult Education Centre, Stretford Road, Manchester M15 5FQ
Printed by RAP, 201 Spotland Road, Rochdale
ISBN 0 906253 65 9
British Library cataloguing in publication data:
A catalogue record for this book is available from the British Library

This book was developed from writing produced originally between Angela Roscoe and her tutor, Jill Barnett at Rackhouse Centre.

Two Gatehouse Book Selection Groups recommended this story for publication. Many thanks for their work to Nora Ashton, Irene Leech, Mary Morris and Josie Roche at Newton House & Sandra Brown, Beverley Chadderton, Christine Jones, Gail Rocca, John Smith, Kevin Summers and Hugh Walsh at Spurley Hey Centre

Thanks also to basic skills groups run by Manchester Adult Education Services at The Birtles, Greenheys, Newton House, Plant Hill and Varna Centres and to Moya Curran's group in Stockport with whom we piloted a first draft of this book

Gatehouse also acknowledges continued financial support from Manchester City Council and North West Arts Board and support from Manchester Adult Education Services (MAES)

# Introduction

## Why I went back into education

Up until about three years ago
I didn't realise I had a problem with my education.
I'd always worked in factories
and I'd never had to sit and write anything down.
Then, my son, Steven had to go into school.
So I got a part-time job in school
as a lunchtime organiser.
I was fine until I had to start writing out reports
and the teachers had to read them.
It made me embarrassed because of my spellings.
I decided to go to Rackhouse Centre
to improve on my English.
I met Jill Barnett, the English teacher,
who gave me confidence and encouragement.

## How I came to write this story

Jill asked me to write a story
about what had happened while I was off on holiday.
I had to write it about three times
before we got the spellings and punctuation sorted out.
Then she said, "Just add a bit to the end
because the story just stops." I did that.
I had to rewrite it and get the corrections done.
I put it on the computer to make sure it looked alright.
Jill said that she was going to send it to Gatehouse.
That's it. I thought I'd never hear anything of it again!

Angela Roscoe

Up until last week
I have always wanted a dog
but not any more.

Janice, my friend
asked me would I mind BJ
her golden labrador.
"Sure, no problem," I said.
Janice explained
she was going to Wales
for the week, with her family.
And the dog would fret
if she put it in kennels.
"Just bring him over Saturday morning
and he'll be fine," I said.

tchen.

up.

*yway?*

My children, Billy and Steven
were so excited
they were up at seven.
I wouldn’t mind,
but Janice and Keith weren’t going
till 12 o’clock.

Steven shouted
"Mum, here’s Janice with BJ."



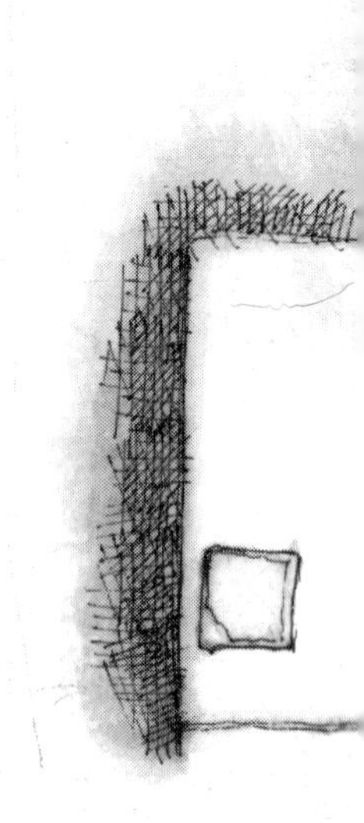

As we entered the hous
BJ shot straight into the
Whoosh!
The cat food was gobbl
The cat was not amuse
Then, *Who’s house is it*
The dog was barking.
The cat was hissing.
The kids were screamir
I was bawling.

I could see what sort of a week
I was going to have.

One deep breath
and then I sorted it all out.
BJ went into the back garden
with the kids
while I fed the cat.

When the cat had finished
she went out the front door.
BJ came back in through the back door.

Two hours later ...

The kids must have got fed up with BJ

and went out on their bikes.

I was getting the tea ready,

thinking to myself,

BJ has settled down nice.

Until I went into the living room.

He had chewed one of my shoes up and Action Man's* leg.



*toy soldier

I wasn't bothered about my shoe.
It was old, anyway
but how was I going to explain
to Steven about his best mate?

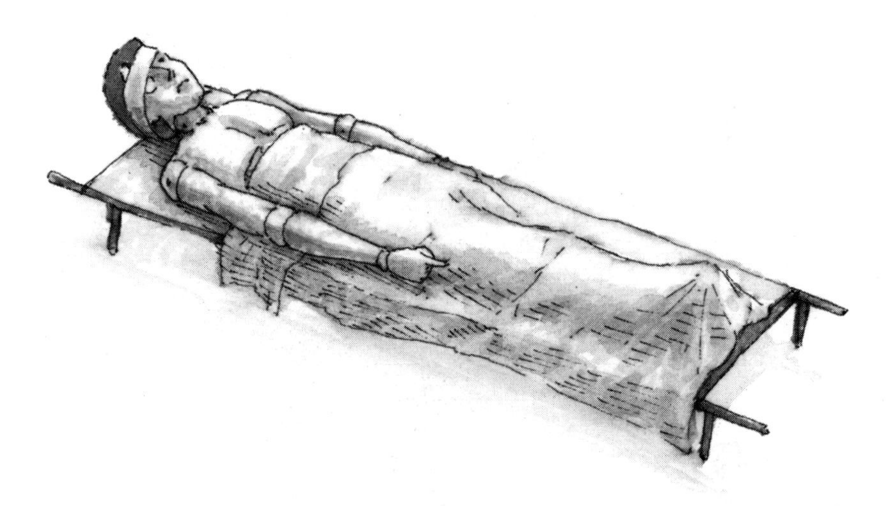

Quick thinking on my behalf.
I put Action Man on a stretcher,
put lipstick on some cotton wool
and told Steven
he had been to war
and he had stood on a land mine.

He thought it was brilliant
and played for hours after
with his Action Man toys.
BJ was locked in the garden
until night time.

This week was an experience.
Never again!

But then BJ would come up to me
with his sad eyes
and then I would say
"Well, maybe."

The rest of the week
wasn’t that bad, actually.
Sophie, the cat, didn’t agree though.
I think she had run out of hisses.
She had left home
and moved into the shed
out of the way.

Hurray, Saturday morning.
Janice's car pulls up.
BJ shoots out of the door
one hundred miles an hour,
straight up to Janice and Keith
wagging his tail.
I think I could hear BJ saying
"Thank God, you're home."
And then you could hear me saying
"Thank God, you're home."

"Back to normal, " I said to myself
until I heard these famous words
"Mum, can we have a dog?"
"No," I said.
"Oh, why not Mum?"

Help, how do I get out of this one?

# Gatehouse Books

**Gatehouse is a unique publisher**

Our writers are adults who are developing their basic reading and writing skills. Their ideas and experiences make fascinating material for any reader, but are particularly relevant for adults working on their reading and writing skills. The writing strikes a chord - a shared experience of struggling against many odds.

The format of our books is clear and uncluttered. The language is familiar and the text is often line-broken, so that each line ends at a natural pause.

Gatehouse books are both popular and respected within Adult Basic Education throughout the English speaking world. They are also a valuable resource within secondary schools, Special Needs Education, Social Services and within the Prison Education and Probation services.

# Booklist Available

Gatehouse Books
Hulme Adult Education Centre
Stretford Road
Manchester M15 5FQ
Tel/Fax: 0161 226 7152
The Gatehouse Publishing Charity is a registered charity reg. no. 1011042
Gatehouse Books Ltd., is a company limited by guarantee, reg no. 2619614